CR

11/01-4
30
45

2001

THE STATES AND THEIR SYMBOLS

Hawaii
Facts and Symbols

by Emily McAuliffe

Consultant:
Roy K. Alameida
Teacher, Social Studies
Kamehameha Schools,
Honolulu, Hawaii

Hilltop Books
an imprint of Capstone Press
Mankato, Minnesota

Hilltop Books are published by Capstone Press
818 North Willow Street, Mankato, Minnesota 56001
http://www.capstone-press.com

Library of Congress Cataloging-in-Publication Data
McAuliffe, Emily.
    Hawaii facts and symbols/by Emily McAuliffe.
    p. cm.—(States and their symbols)
    Includes bibliographical references (p. 23) and index.
    Summary: Presents information about the state of Hawaii, its nickname, motto,
and emblems.
    ISBN 0-7368-0375-0
    1. Emblems, State—Hawaii—Juvenile literature. [1. Emblems, State—Hawaii.
2. Hawaii.] I. Title. II. Series: McAuliffe, Emily. States and their symbols.
CR203.H3M33 2000
996.9′0022—dc21   99—19768
                                                                          CIP

Editorial Credits
Damian Koshnick, editor; Heather Kindseth, cover designer; Linda Clavel, illustrator;
    Kimberly Danger, photo researcher

Photo Credits
Corbis, 6
Doris J. Brookes, 22 (middle)
Hawaii Visitors' Bureau/Lindy Boyes, 14
Index Stock Imagery/Tom Walker, 18
Innerspace Visions/Michael S. Nolan, cover
International Stock/Tom Till, 16
James P. Rowan, 12
John Elk III, 10, 22 (bottom)
Norbert Wu/www.norbertwu.com, 20
One Mile Up Inc., 8, 10 (inset)
Visuals Unlimited/Nancy L. Cushing, 22 (top)

Table of Contents

Kauai

Pacific Ocean

Oahu

Honolulu

U.S.S. Arizona
at Pearl Harbor

Molokai

Road to Hana

Maui

HAWAII

Hawaii

Hilo ●

Mauna Loa   Kilauea

Hawaii Volcanoes
National Park

Canada

Pacific
Ocean

United States

Mexico

HAWAIIAN
ISLANDS

⭐	Capital
○	City
🏛	Places to Visit
〰	Road
🌋	Volcano

Capital: Honolulu is the capital of Hawaii.

Largest City: Honolulu is the largest city in Hawaii. About 386,000 people live in Honolulu.

Size: Hawaii's eight main islands cover 6,459 square miles (16,729 square kilometers). Hawaii is the 47th largest state.

Location: Hawaii is in the central Pacific Ocean.

Population: About 1,193,000 people live in Hawaii (U.S. Census Bureau, 1998 estimate).

Statehood: Hawaii became the 50th state on August 21, 1959.

Natural Resources: People catch fish in the Pacific Ocean near Hawaii. Visitors admire Hawaii's landscape.

Manufactured Goods: Hawaiians make clay, glass, and stone products. They also make clothing.

Crops: Farmers in Hawaii grow macadamia nuts, pineapples, sugar cane, and coffee beans. They also raise cattle.

State Name and Nickname

The name Hawaii comes from the Polynesian (pahl-ee-NEE-zhun) people. The Polynesians discovered Hawaii between 1,400 and 1,700 years ago. They canoed from their homeland 2,000 miles (3,219 kilometers) south of Hawaii.

Some people think the name Hawaii comes from a Polynesian man named Hawaii Loa. Hawaii Loa is believed to have first discovered the Hawaiian Islands. Other people believe the name Hawaii comes from the word Hawaiki. Hawaiki is a Polynesian word that means small homeland.

In 1778, British explorer James Cook became the first European to discover Hawaii. During his stay, Cook traded with the native Hawaiians. Cook's men gave the Hawaiians metal for fish and supplies.

In 1959, Hawaiians chose "The Aloha State" as the state's official nickname. Aloha is the Hawaiian word for welcome, good-bye, and love.

In 1778, British explorer James Cook arrived in Hawaii. Polynesians lived in Hawaii long before his arrival.

State Seal and Motto

Hawaii adopted its state seal in 1959. The state seal reminds Hawaiians of their state government. The seal also makes government papers official.

Hawaii's state seal shows a shield in the center. Pictures of taro and banana leaves are below the shield. They represent the native plants of Hawaii.

King Kamehameha I (kuh-may-hah-MAY-hah) is to the left of the shield. This famous Hawaiian king was the first to unite the Hawaiian Islands. Hawaiians remember him on King Kamehameha Day. They celebrate this day on June 11.

The goddess of liberty is to the right of the shield. She stands for Hawaiian freedom.

King Kamehameha III chose the Hawaiian motto in 1843. The motto is "The life of the land is perpetuated in righteousness." The state motto refers to Great Britain's return of the Hawaiian kingdom to its native people.

The state motto is shown on the state seal. In Hawaiian, the motto is Ua mau ke ea o ka aina i ka pono.

State Capitol and Flag

Honolulu is Hawaii's capital city. The state capitol building is in Honolulu. Government officials meet in the capitol to make the state's laws. Workers built Hawaii's capitol from 1965 to 1969. The capitol is made of concrete and steel.

The capitol's design reminds people of Hawaii's landscape. The top of the building is shaped like a volcano. This shape reminds people that volcanoes formed the Hawaiian Islands. Large columns surround the capitol. They stand for Hawaii's royal palm trees. A pool of water circles the capitol. The pool makes the capitol look like it is on an island.

Hawaii's state flag has eight stripes. Each stripe is either red, white, or blue. These stripes stand for Hawaii's eight main islands. The upper left corner of Hawaii's flag looks like the British flag. It reminds Hawaiians of their past ties to Great Britain.

The capitol's roof is shaped like a volcano. Long ago, lava from volcanoes dried to form the Hawaiian Islands in the Pacific Ocean.

State Bird

The nene (NAY-nay) became Hawaii's state bird in 1957. Nene make a "nay nay" sound when they eat. Nene are found only in Hawaii. Some people call nene Hawaiian geese.

Nene have long, cream-colored necks with black stripes. The birds have black heads and gray-brown bodies. Adult nene weigh about 5 pounds (2.3 kilograms). Nene build their nests on the slopes of volcanoes. Their claws help them walk on the rocky lava.

Today, life is difficult for the nene. Dogs, rats, and mongeese prey on the nene. These animals are not native to Hawaii. People brought them from other parts of the world. Now the nene must compete with these animals to survive.

By 1950, only 30 nene were left in Hawaii. Since then, Hawaiians have worked to protect this bird. More than 2,000 nene now live on the islands.

Nene eat grass, seeds, flowers, leaves, and fruit.

State Tree

Hawaii adopted the kukui (KOO-koo-wee) as its state tree in 1959. Kukui trees are common throughout Hawaii. They can grow to be 50 feet (15 meters) tall.

Kukui trees have pointed leaves that are a light, silver-green color. This color comes from the soft, silver fuzz that grows on the leaves. Small white flowers and nuts also grow on kukui trees.

Native Hawaiians used parts of the kukui tree as medicine. They treated sores with kukui nut oil. They treated bruises with kukui leaves.

Native Hawaiians burned the oil from kukui nuts for light. They put many kukui nuts on a stick. The burning oil in the nuts looked like candles. The kukui tree also is called the candlenut tree.

Kukui nuts still are a traditional Hawaiian food. People roast the nuts. They then mash the kukui nuts and flavor them with salt.

Kukui trees grow throughout Hawaii. Kukui trees are easy to spot in forests because of their light green color.

State Flower

Hawaiians named the yellow hibiscus the state flower in 1923. Hibiscus flowers are large and come in hundreds of types and colors. In Hawaiian, the yellow hibiscus is called the Pua Aloala (POOA ALO-ala).

Hibiscus plants look like small trees or bushes. Hibiscus plants grow to be 5 to 30 feet (1.5 to 9 meters) tall. Yellow hibiscus flowers have five large, thin petals. Their blossoms can be 6 inches (15 centimeters) wide. A long pistil grows from the center of the blossom. This helps the hibiscus make seeds that will eventually grow into new plants.

The yellow hibiscus is native to the Hawaiian Islands. This plant once grew throughout Hawaii. Today, fewer than 300 wild, yellow hibiscus plants survive on the three main islands of Hawaii, Maui, and Lanai.

Hibiscus plants grow in warm, shaded areas. Hibiscus blooms last about 2 to 3 days.

State Marine Mammal

The humpback whale was named Hawaii's state marine mammal in 1979. Hawaii is the only state that has more ocean mammals than land mammals.

Humpback whales grow to be about 50 feet (15 meters) long. They have large fins that look like wings. Their fins can grow up to 12 feet (3.6 meters) long. Whales use fins to swim and to leap out of the water.

Humpback whales have baleen instead of teeth. These small plates help whales filter food out of the ocean. Humpbacks eat mostly small fish and plankton.

Humpback whales do not live near Hawaii all year. They visit Hawaii in the winter to give birth. The whales live in colder northern waters the rest of the year. Whale watching is popular in Hawaii. Humpback whales sometimes swim close to boats.

Humpback whales often breach. They lift themselves out of the water with their large fins.

More State Symbols

Native State Language: In 1978, Hawaiian became the official native language of Hawaii. Hawaii is the only state that has an official native language.

State Fish: The rectangular triggerfish is Hawaii's official state fish. The fish's nickname is the pig-snouted triggerfish. It has a nose that looks like a pig snout. The fish also grunts when it is in danger.

State Gem: Hawaii officials named black coral the state gem in 1987. Black coral grows underwater. People make jewelry from black coral. Today, black coral is rare. Coral grows slowly. Many people now think the coral should be left in its natural setting.

State Team Sport: Outrigger canoe paddling became Hawaii's state team sport in 1986. An outrigger canoe is a narrow boat with a long rail on one side. The rail helps the canoe balance in ocean waves.

The triggerfish is known as humuhumunukunukuapua'a in the Hawaiian language.

Places to Visit

Hawaii Volcanoes National Park

Hawaii Volcanoes National Park is on the island of Hawaii. This park features the Kilauea and Mauna Loa Volcanoes. Kilauea is the world's most active volcano. Visitors see lava flows and a live fire pit. Visitors also hike, camp, and star gaze on the volcanoes.

Road to Hana

The road to Hana is on the Hawiian island of Maui. The road winds along steep, forested cliffs. People often travel the road to see the many natural sites on the way to the town of Hana. Visitors see waterfalls, native plants, and ocean views along the way.

U.S.S. *Arizona* Memorial

The U.S.S. *Arizona* Memorial is in Hawaii's Pearl Harbor. In 1941, Japan bombed Pearl Harbor. The U.S.S. *Arizona* sank and its 1,100 crew members died. Visitors can take a ferry into the harbor to see the sunken ship.

Words to Know

baleen (BAY-leen)—plates in a whale's mouth that help it eat

mammal (MAM-uhl)—a warm-blooded animal; mammals feed milk to their young.

Polynesian (pall-ee-NEE-zhun)—a person or language from the Pacific Islands of Polynesia

taro (TAHR-o)—a plant with roots that people eat

volcano (val-KAY-noh)—a mountain with vents through which hot gas and lava sometimes erupt

Read More

Fradin, Dennis B. *Hawaii.* From Sea to Shining Sea. Chicago: Children's Press, 1994.

Johnston, Joyce. *Hawaii.* Hello U.S.A. Minneapolis: Lerner Publications, 1995.

Kummer, Patricia K. *Hawaii.* One Nation. Mankato, Minn.: Capstone Press, 1998.

Useful Addresses

Hawaii Department of Tourism
P.O. Box 2359
Honolulu, HI 96804

Hawaii State Library
478 South King Street
Honolulu, HI 96813

Internet Sites

Hawaii
http://pacificgold.com/state/default.htm
Hawaii Information for School Reports
http://www.gohawaii.com/hokeo/school/report.html
Hawaii State Symbols
http://50states.com/hawaii.htm

Index